Changing Shape

Think about the materials you have touched today.

1. **Which materials change shape easily?**

   _____

2. **Which materials do not change shape easily?**

   _____

3. **Work in a pair to finish these sentences. You can use words or pictures to help you. The first sentence has been done for you.**

You can change the shape of a *ruler* by *bending* it.

You can change the shape of a _____ by _____ it.

You can change the shape of a _____ by _____ it.

You can change the shape of a _____ by _____ it.

You can change the shape of a _____ by _____ it.

Change the Shape

1 Look at the diagrams. Then draw a circle around the materials that you think will change shape easily.

Modelling clay

Rocks

Wool

Scissors

Cushion

Elastic bands

Tree trunks

Metal girder

How Was it Changed?

Look at the items below.

1. Think about how their shape has been changed.

2. Sort the items by how they have changed shape in the table below.

Stretched	Bent	Squashed	Twisted

Changing Materials to Make Things

1 Match each material to something that is made from it. The first one has been done for you.

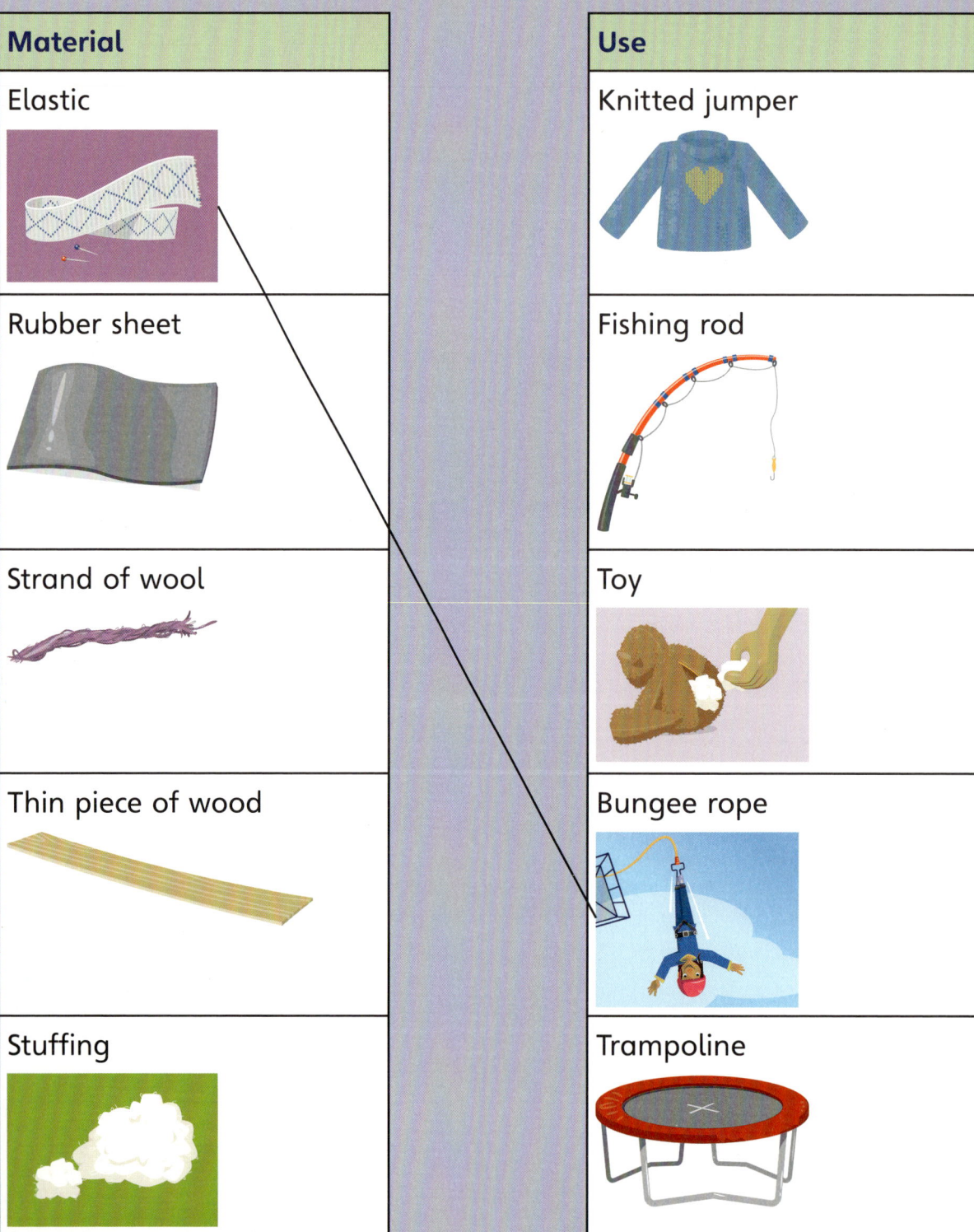

Terrible Trampolines

A trampoline uses lots of stretchy materials.

1. What would be the worst material you could use to make a trampoline?

   _____

2. Why is your choice such a poor material for a trampoline?

   _____
   _____

3. What materials would not be very good for making a bungee cord, or a balloon?

   _____
   _____

Science Skills

Stretchy Putty Races – Graph it!

Isla and Vash have made their own stretchy putty. They want to find out whose putty stretches fastest.

They made sure they both had the same amount of putty.

They marked out a starting line at the top of the window.

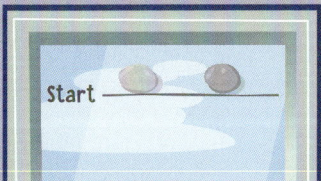

They each placed their putty on the start line.

They recorded their results every two minutes.

Here are the results from their putty race:

	Time from start (minutes)							
	2	4	6	8	10	12	14	16
Distance stretched Isla (cm)	1 cm	2 cm	4 cm	6 cm	7 cm	8 cm	10 cm	12 cm
Distance stretched Vash (cm)	1 cm	1.5 cm	3 cm	4 cm	5 cm	6 cm	8 cm	10 cm

Changing Shape

1 Whose putty won the race?

2 How far did the winning putty stretch?

3 Finish the graph to show how quickly the winning putty stretched.

Distance stretched (cm) / Time from start (minutes)

Using Rubber

Rubber is used today to make thousands of things that we use every day.

1. How many things can you think of that are made from rubber?
   Use words and pictures to record your ideas.

Bendy

This bridge is made of strong metal that does not bend. Imagine the bridge is made of a bendy material such as rubber.

1. What would happen when cars and lorries drive over it?

   _____

2. Where else is it a bad idea to use bendy materials? Draw a picture of something that you think should not be bendy.

3. What would happen if this object was bendy?

   _____

Science Skills

Bendy Ruler – Predict it!

1 Which ruler do you think is the most bendy?

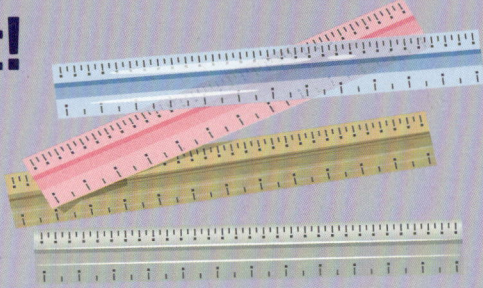

_____

2 Put the rulers in order from most bendy to least bendy. Draw them here.

Most bendy   **Least bendy**

Work with a partner to test the rulers. Carefully bend the rulers. If you bend them too much they might snap! Talk with your partner about your results.

3 What did you discover?
  Did you get the rulers in the right order?
  What surprised you when you tested the rulers?

_____

Science Skills

Exploring Materials – Record it!

Twisting, weaving and knitting are often used to make fabric. Use a hand lens or microscope to look closely at your clothes. Do they all look the same?

1   Record what you see in the spaces below and write the name of each material you observe.

Material 1:

Material 2:

Material 3:

Paper Weaving

You will need two different coloured sheets of paper. Follow the steps shown here to weave a paper mat of your own!

Take a piece of paper and fold it in half.

Mark 2 cm spaces along the folded edge.

Cut straight lines from the folded edge almost to the end opposite edge. Do not cut all the way across.

Cut the other piece of paper into strips of approx. 2 cm wide.

Open out the first piece of paper. Take strips of the second paper and weave them through the slots on the first piece of paper.

Use more strips and keep weaving until your mat is complete.

Science Skills

Amazing Balloons – Investigate it!

You can change the shape of a balloon in lots of different ways. Did you know that if you sit carefully on a blown up balloon it will not pop? Balloons are very squashy!

Let's carry out a test to find out which other materials will squash.

1 Write or draw the objects you test in the spaces below, sorting them by whether they squashed or not.

2 Which materials squashed the most?

_____

3 Which materials changed the least?

_____

Making Modelling Dough

Use the words at the bottom of the page to help complete the sentences.

1. Mix the _____ and the _____ together.

2. Add _____. If you add too little the dough will be _____ and crumbly. If you add too much the dough will be too _____.

3. Mix the ingredients until the dough becomes _____ and _____.

4. Once you have made your model you can leave it to _____.

5. It will take a few days for the dough to dry out and _____.

6. Once dry you can use _____ to decorate your models.

dry   flour   harden   paint   salt
soft   squashy   sticky   water

Odd One Out

Look at the objects below. For each question draw a circle around the odd one out.

1

Explain your answer.

_____
_____

2

Explain your answer.

_____
_____

3

Explain your answer.

_____
_____

What I Have Learned

Think about what you have learned in this unit.

1   What was the most interesting part and why?

2   What else would you have liked to find out about?